Merry Christmas 195*

First Methodist Church
Laramie, Wyoming

Peggy

Peggy Lynn Falgien

THE STORIES IN THIS BOOK

The author, Mary Alice Jones, is a well-known leading authority in the field of religious education. As Director of Children's Work for the International Council of Religious Education for many years, she has been in constant touch with thousands of children and teachers and parents all over the country. She has written many religious books for children, and has achieved great success in the retelling of beloved Bible stories so that children want to hear them again and again.

Bible Stories

OLD TESTAMENT

By MARY ALICE JONES

Illustrated by ELIZABETH WEBBE

RAND McNALLY & COMPANY · **Chicago**

Joseph Goes on an Errand

Joseph lived in a large family. He had ten big brothers and one little brother.

Now, Joseph's father had many, many sheep. His sons helped him take care of them. When there was grass and water near their father's tents, Joseph went with his big brothers to feed and water the sheep. But sometimes the sheep had to be taken far from home to find enough grass and water.

These long trips took many days, and only the big brothers went along. Joseph wanted to go but he knew he must wait until his father told him he was big enough. So he stayed near his father's tents with his little brother.

One time the big brothers were away days and days. Joseph knew his father was worried.

Then early one morning his father called Joseph. "Your brothers have been gone a long time. They are feeding the flocks near Shechem. You are big enough, now, to go on an errand away from home. You know how to get to Shechem. Go and find your brothers and see how they are getting along so that I may have word of them."

Joseph was glad his father thought he was big enough to go on an errand by himself.

"Yes, Father, I will go for you. I will start right away."

So Joseph started toward Shechem. He walked and walked. It was hot. He grew tired. Finally, he came to Shechem. Then he looked and looked. But he could not find his brothers.

A man saw the boy wandering about the fields.

"Whom are you looking for?" he asked.

"I am looking for my brothers who are feeding our father's flocks. But I cannot find them."

"I know where they are," the man told Joseph. "They left here a few days ago. I heard them say, 'Let us go to Dothan.'"

The man showed Joseph the way to Dothan, and on and on Joseph went.

By and by he came to Dothan. The man was right! His brothers had come to Dothan. Joseph saw them, and he saw the sheep eating grass on the hillside.

So Joseph found his brothers. As he ran forward to meet them, Joseph was feeling proud of having done the errand his father had asked him to do.

Miriam and Her Baby Brother

Once there was a wicked king. He did not like some of the people in his country. So he passed a law to hurt them. The law said that whenever a baby boy was born to them, the baby should be taken away.

In one family there was a girl whose name was Miriam. Then a baby brother was born.

"Oh, Mother, we must think of a way to hide our baby," Miriam said.

So Miriam and her mother thought and thought.

"We will make a little cradle boat, snug and tight so the water can't get in," the mother said. "Then we will wrap the baby in a blanket and put the little cradle boat in the tall grass at the edge of the river."

Miriam clapped her hands. "What a wonder-

ful plan, Mother! No one will think of looking there! And if the baby cries, no one can hear him."

Quickly Miriam and her mother carried out their plan. Then Miriam said, "I will hide here on the river bank to watch the baby."

Everything was quiet. Then Miriam heard voices. Peeping out from the tall grass, she saw the princess, the daughter of the wicked king. And the princess had seen the cradle boat!

"What is that?" she asked one of the girls with her. "Go and bring it to me."

While Miriam trembled, the girl brought the little cradle boat from the river. The princess moved the blanket and saw the baby cuddled inside. And the baby cried.

"What a dear baby!" the princess said. Then her face grew sad as she remembered the wicked law. "Some mother is trying to hide her baby," she whispered.

Then the princess spoke again. "I will adopt this baby myself. No one will dare take him away when I say he is the son of the princess."

Miriam ran out from the high grasses. She had a plan! "The princess is too young to take care of a baby," she began politely. "I know a good nurse."

The princess smiled. "Bring the good nurse to me," she said.

So Miriam ran to her own home. She told her mother all that had happened. And the mother hurried to the princess.

"I have found this baby near the river's edge," the princess explained. "I am going to adopt him as my own. And I am going to name him Moses. But I need a good nurse. Will you take care of the baby for me?"

And so the baby's own mother took care of the baby Moses. And the baby grew and was safe and happy.

Ruth and Naomi

Ruth was a stranger in the town of Bethlehem. She had come from her own country to take care of her mother-in-law Naomi. For Naomi was old, and Ruth loved her very much.

Now, Ruth and Naomi were poor. They had no money to buy food.

Early one morning Ruth went to the fields where the young men and women of Bethlehem were working to gather the ripe grain. She spoke timidly to the man in charge. "Please," she said, "may I gather the fallen grain in the fields?"

The man had heard that Ruth had come to Bethlehem to take care of Naomi. So he spoke kindly to her. "Yes, you may glean. Watch the other girls and do as they do."

So Ruth began to gather the grain. All morning she worked, without resting even for a moment. About noon Boaz, the owner of the field, came. He, too, spoke kindly to Ruth.

"Stop working now and then," he told her, "and drink the water which the young men have drawn. And when mealtime comes, eat with the others."

"You are very kind to me, a stranger," Ruth answered.

Boaz spoke again. "I have heard all that you have done for your mother-in-law Naomi. May God help you and comfort you."

When mealtime came, Ruth went in to eat. As she ate the good food, she thought of Naomi at home with so little to eat. "They have given me more food than I need," she said to herself. "I will save some of my portion and take it home to Naomi."

Then Ruth went back to the fields and worked all afternoon.

When the day's work was done, she hurried

home. "See," she called to Naomi, "see the good grain I worked for!" And she poured the grain into the vessel Naomi had ready.

Then she brought out her surprise. "And, see, I saved some of the good lunch they gave me. I saved it for you."

So Ruth and Naomi had food for supper that night. And they had food for supper every night. Because Boaz had told Ruth that she could glean in his field every day.

David and the Sheep

David was a shepherd. He took care of his father's sheep.

Many boys would have been lonely. The place where the sheep were kept was far from the town. Many times David stayed all night in the hills with only the sheep for company.

But David was not lonely. The sunrise and the sunset and the clouds and the brooks and the stars at night made him feel close to God. Often he made up poems about the things he saw about him. He had a little harp and he played happy tunes. Sometimes he made tunes for the poems he had written and he would sing them as songs of praise to God.

David's job was to take care of the sheep. He looked for good grass for his flock. He found pools of water where it was safe for his sheep to drink. And when the sun was hot, he led them to shady places to rest.

One night David was making soft music on his little harp. The sheep were all about him, fast asleep. Suddenly David saw a shadow move. It was not the shadow of a restless sheep. It was not the shadow of a tree moved by the night breeze. It was the shadow of a lion! And the lion was moving toward a little lamb.

David laid his harp on a rock. His feet seemed not to touch the ground so swiftly did he move toward the lamb. The lion was very near. But David was nearer! He reached the little lamb and lifted him into the shelter of his arms. Then

he reached for a large piece of rock and turned toward the lion.

The great beast seemed to know that David was not afraid of him. He seemed to know that David was not going to let him get near any of his sheep. As the rock came flying toward him, the lion gave a parting roar and dashed away into the night.

The sheep waked up. They ran about, frightened. Then they heard David's voice, speaking to them. It was the voice they trusted. They stopped running around.

As the sheep became quiet, David put the little lamb back in the flock. Then he picked up his harp and began playing soft tunes. The sheep felt safe now. They knew their shepherd was taking care of them. And soon they were all asleep again.

Elisha's Room on the Roof

Once there was a good man named Elisha who went about the country helping people. Elisha had no home of his own. Sometimes when he was tired after a long journey, he would say to him-

all my own!"

One day, as Elisha was walking through the
town of Shunem, he passed by a large house
where a rich man and his wife lived. The woman
saw Elisha as he passed, looking hot and tired.
She had heard how he traveled about the country

helping people. So she went out to meet him.

"Come into my house and rest a while, and let me give you some cool water and some food."

So Elisha went in and rested and ate. After that, whenever he was near Shunem, the woman invited him to come to her house to rest and eat.

One day, as she watched Elisha walk away, the woman spoke to her husband.

"Elisha is such a good man," she began. "He helps so many people. And he does not have a place that is home. I think it would be a good plan if we built a little room for him, a room that would be all his own."

"Where would we build it?" the husband asked.

"Right on our flat roof," the wife answered. "We could build a stairway outside so he could come and go whenever he wanted to."

"Yes, that would be a good plan," the husband agreed.

So the woman called the workmen. "I want a pleasant room," she told them. "And I want the room to have a bed and a table and a chair and a lamp."

The workmen began planning right away. And the next time Elisha came to Shunem, the woman and her husband led him up the outside

stairway and opened the door to the room on the roof. Elisha saw the pretty new room and the bed and the table and the chair and the lamp.

And then the woman said, "It is yours. It is all yours, Elisha. It is your own home."

How surprised and pleased Elisha was!

And he thanked the woman and her husband. And he came often to the little room. How good it was to have a home of his own!